John Paul Jackson

Moments with God℠

Dream Journal

Streams Publications
North Sutton, New Hampshire

"**God** may **speak** in one way,
or in another, yet man does not
perceive it. In a dream, in a
vision of the night, when **deep**
sleep falls upon men,
while slumbering on their beds,
then **He opens** the ears of men,
and seals their **instruction**."

– Job 33:14-16

This dream journal belongs to:

_____
Name

_____
Address

_____

Date:

_____
From

_____
To

Hearing God's Whispers

As He did with generations before us, God speaks to us in dreams and visions while we sleep (Job 33:14-15). Forever mindful of us, God faithfully guides us day and night because, unlike us, He never slumbers (Psalm 121:3-4).

An ancient wisdom of God is being released to us today. God is pouring out His Spirit in greater measure and accelerating the use of dreams to speak with mankind (Joel 2:28; Acts 2:17-19). It is a means of divine communication that we would be wise not to ignore. One third of the Bible deals directly or indirectly with this means of communication from God.

A dream's impact on our lives, and on the lives of those around us, can be profound. Dreams have caused kings to scour the Earth for an interpretation. Nations have been conquered, inventions have been discovered, solutions have been found, and lives have been changed all because of these night parables called dreams.

A dream journal is a wonderful way to chronicle the insights God whispers during the night. By keeping a dream journal, you will be able to see the Lord's faithfulness in guiding you through life. Threads of His involvement will become evident, as you live and move and have your being in Him (Acts 17:28).

If you commit to journaling your dreams, God will increase the number of your dreams. He honors your inquiry and interest in studying your dreams by unfolding more spiritual insights. Remember, God rewards those who diligently seek Him.

If you seek the Lord your God, you will find Him if you seek Him with all your heart and with all your soul.

—DEUTERONOMY 4:29b

I love those who love me, and those who seek me diligently will find me. —PROVERBS 8:17

Ask and it will be given to you; seek, and you will find; knock, and it will be opened to you. For everyone who asks receives, and he who seeks finds, and to him who knocks it will be opened.

—MATTHEW 7:7-8

Over the years, I have learned to treasure my dreams. I have also coached many people on how to interpret their own dreams. While I don't profess to hold all the answers to what every symbol means, I do have suggestions on how you can more skillfully interpret your dreams. As you begin the adventure of deciphering these nightly treasures, I hope you will have as much fun as I've had unearthing their secrets.

The Uniqueness of This Dream Journal

In designing this dream journal, I wanted to enhance your power of observation and recognition, and offer key questions to help you unlock a dream's meaning. Most dreams can be understood by following a few simple guidelines.

I also wanted to reinforce the Holy Spirit's role in helping you interpret a dream. He greatly desires to reveal to you the deep things of God. Remember, God wants to spend time with you! As you spend time with Him uncovering the secrets of your dreams, you will delight in discovering the God-given destiny that awaits you.

A Few Suggestions

1. Upon waking from a dream, pick up your dream journal and fill in the **date**. Dreams are written in our minds with disappearing ink. If we do not re-experience them immediately—by allowing time to pass before writing them down—our dreams will quickly fade from memory. Key elements may become lost and irretrievable.

2. Give your dream a **title**. Naming your dream helps you later recall its contents. For example, if you dreamed about a devastating tidal wave that wreaked havoc and brought loss of life,

you could title your dream, "A Killer Wave." Some people like to group their dreams by title rather than by date.

3. Consider the dream's **theme**. What is the main subject or plot of your dream? Look for the prevailing action or interaction in the dream. Were you impatient? Were there many changes or shifts in location?

4. Notice where you are in the dream. Are you **observing** from a place where you can see what is going on, but others do not see you? Or, are you walking among them? If you are observing, it indicates the dream is about someone or something other than yourself. Most of the time when you are observing, you are doing so from a high place as if you are standing on some sort of platform.

   Are you **participating** in the dream? This is where you are involved in the dream, but the dream revolves around someone or something other than you. These dreams are usually about something you are involved in and therefore, may have an indirect impact on you.

   Or, are you the **center of activity**? If you are the focus of the dream, then the activity will revolve around you. The dream will center on something in your life or something you will encounter.

5. Who or what is the **focus** or center of attention in your dream? The focus of the dream may be determined by a simple test: Ask yourself if this person or object were removed from the dream, would the dream still exist? Would the dream still make sense?

6. What are the **sub-focuses** (additional emphases) in your dream? Dreams may have more than one sub-focus. These elements offer descriptive details that add atmosphere and insight to your dream's interpretation.

7. What **colors** are present in your dream? Is the dream in color or black-and-white? Are the colors vibrant or muted? Many people dream in color, but the color details escape them and they are left with the impression their dream is in black-and-white. Some only remember an element that is shaded in a color.

Colors are probably the most over-looked element in our dreams. When colors appear in our dreams, it is usually because they mean something or they will aid us in understanding the dream's interpretation. The first sign (the rainbow) God gave to mankind was in color. Why didn't God give us a black-and-white rainbow? The colors of the stones on the priest's ephod are twelve distinct and different colors (Exodus 28).

God speaks to us in colors all the time. Colors fill the descriptions of Heaven. Never is God present in Scripture without the mention of color. Just look at all the colors in creation. Doesn't that tell you God is *really* into color!

In this packet, you will find three color wheels: Additive, Subtractive, and the Additive and Subtractive color spectrums. In the Additive (Spirit) color spectrum, primary colors of red, green, and blue combine with secondary colors of yellow, cyan, and magenta. These are the only color combinations that produce white light. In the Subtractive (Soul) color spectrum, primary colors of yellow, cyan, and magenta combine with secondary colors of red, green, and blue, producing black or dark light. In addition, there is also an artist color spectrum in which the colors represent the body (flesh). However, I am not going to discuss that here. (For more about the colors of God, please see pages 21-25).

8. Is your dream **recurring**? Have you had the dream over a period of time? Recurring dreams contain important themes and deserve special attention.

© 2002 John Paul Jackson

9. Determine the dream **category**. There are 20 categories of dreams:

Healing Dreams	Flushing Dreams
Calling Dreams	Warning Dreams
False Dreams	Body Dreams
Chemical Dreams	Self-Condition Dreams
Courage Dreams	Correction Dreams
Direction Dreams	Intercession Dreams
Prophecy & Revelation Dreams	Dark Dreams
Spiritual Warfare Dreams	Fear Dreams
Invention Dreams	Word of Knowledge Dreams
Deliverance Dreams	Soul Dreams

Dreams can inspire inventions and solutions to problems. Dreams can provide direction and warn us of impending danger. They can change and inform us. Each type of dream is designed by the Lord to help us, or someone else, get to a place He created for us and to expand the Kingdom of God.

10. What is the **context** or overriding feeling you had in the dream? Was it positive or negative? Understanding the context helps you know if you should interpret the symbols or dream elements from the positive or negative side. For example, the color red on the positive side means "anointing" and on the negative side means "anger and war."

Drawing Your Dreams

Drawing or diagramming key elements from a dream is a quick way to record a dream. It also releases **right-brain** (creative) thinking and helps clarify the focus of a dream. For those who find it challenging to function within linear or analytical thinking processes, drawing a dream is helpful.

How a dream is recorded—layout, graphics, placement, and balance—often helps you discover significant details of a dream. Here are some ideas for drawing a dream:

1. Consider **grouping elements** according to movement in time/space or according to strong emotions or feelings.

2. Draw your dream in a **spiral, square**, or **concentric circle** pattern.

3. Emphasize **key words** by writing them in larger or bolder script or by circling, underlining, or placing a wavy line underneath.

4. Consider **mapping** your dream using roads or arrows to show the flow of action.

5. Some find **diagramming** a dream, as you would a sentence in English grammar, quite helpful.

To encourage tapping into your creative right-brain side, I have designed the dream recording portion of this journal with a graph. This allows you to draw, sketch, or record your dream in various shapes. For the "die hards" who resist change, the graphed section also allows you to write your dream in a linear format.

The Interpretive Process

Now take time to **reflect** on a dream's interpretation. Ask the Holy Spirit to help you. He is vital to the interpretive process. Surrender all your soulish insight and wait upon God. You may want to meditate on Scripture or pray. As you open your heart, God's presence will begin to unfold.

God's nightly messages will be **personalized** with images and symbols drawn from your own life experiences. No dream dictionary or fixed-symbol system will give you the perfect meaning of your dream. Dream symbols are helpful, but some will have a meaning that only you understand. While other people may try to shed light on aspects of what a dream's symbol may mean, they may not be able to precisely translate what God intended to communicate to you. Symbols can also have different meanings from dream to dream, depending on the context of the dream.

Learn to **ask yourself questions** in a way that will unlock the meaning of your dreams. Get into the habit of interviewing yourself about important elements of a dream.

1. What **details** did you notice—colors, textures, feelings, smells, order of appearance? What are the most arresting images in the dream? How do you feel about the dream?

2. If you dreamed about a house, **ask** yourself what the house means to you. If people appear in your dream, ask yourself how you feel about them and what they represent to you. Is the person's countenance dark or light? Does the person help or hinder the dream's direction? Has this person appeared in other dreams or in a similar context?

3. How were you **acting**? How were others acting toward you? Were you running from someone? Were you trying to do or say something? What did you feel about what was happening?

By **contrasting** various elements in your dream, you may gain significant understanding about your dream. Ask yourself why God chose to use a particular dream element rather than another element. For example: Why a snake rather than a cow? Why a bicycle rather than a car?

A **vehicle** typically refers to that which God has created and called you to do at that time of your life. A bicycle is smaller than a car and uses a lot of human effort—only one person rides on it. This simple understanding may indicate that your call is small and personal right now. It will require a lot of your effort to get where you are going. As you grow and mature, you will dream less about bicycles; larger vehicles will take their place. However, trains, buses, 747 jetliners, and ships usually symbolize larger things like churches, denominations, or corporations. The context will determine which interpretation to use.

God does not arbitrarily place elements in your dreams. He designates a **specific** element to communicate something of value to you. The use of contrasts allows you to decipher the meaning of many dream elements without having to be an expert in dream interpretation.

Resist going to a book about dream interpretation, especially if it's based on Freudian, Jungian, or other secular psychological concepts. None of these secular interpretation models will allow you to come to the same interpretation of biblical dreams that God gave in Scripture. They will offer a soulish conclusion and can mislead and misdirect you from what God wants to reveal to you.

Reflect on Your Response

Consider what, if any, actions may be appropriate in light of the insights gained from the dream. You may want to reread the dream two or three times during the next week. Your dreams can give you priceless insights, but you must decide how and when to apply them in order to make positive changes in your life. Changing your attitudes and behavior is not easy and it often requires courage.

A dream may **reveal God's plan** for your life. Or, it could reveal Satan's plan to abort God's blessings for you, your family, or your business. I hope what little I've shared here will help you to understand whether your dream is from God or from Satan.

A dream may **reveal a weakness** in your life that God needs to strengthen and heal. You may want to repent and ask God to remove a particular character defect or habit in your life. Sometimes we must be brutally honest in our interpretation of dreams about ourselves. It is very easy to incorrectly interpret a dream, because we deny we have a problem addressed by the dream.

If you feel there was more to your dream and you cannot recall it, **ask God** to increase the intensity and clarity of your dreams. Before falling asleep, ask the Holy Spirit to help you remember or learn the purpose of the dream you will have that night. Imagine the Holy Spirit hovering over you, removing chaos from your life and bringing divine order. Feel the Holy Spirit breathing over you, blowing the dust from your life.

Remember, God wants His Spirit to blanket you and share with you deep spiritual insights (1 Corinthians 2:10). No matter how much you remember, even if you only remember one word, write it down. It may trigger the release of your entire dream.

In Summary

From time-to-time, **review** your dream journal. Notice any spiritual themes that have come to the forefront. The longer you work with your dreams, the more experienced you will become in the various ways in which God speaks.

Knowing more about how and why we dream opens a whole new world of the Spirit to us—one filled with divine insight and revelation. Be patient with yourself as you learn about dream interpretation skills. You may want to consider taking the Streams courses on dreams and visions. Or, you can browse our website (www.streamsministries.com) to watch for our expanded treatment of these glorious, nightly vehicles by which God communicates with us.

Dream explorations often bring thrilling adventures and spiritual insights. As you plunge into the deep truths of God, may you discover wonderful new ideas and ingenious solutions. And may you come to know more intimately how much your heavenly Father really loves you.

Blessings,

John Paul Jackson

Non-Linear Ways To Draw Your Dreams

1. Cluster Method

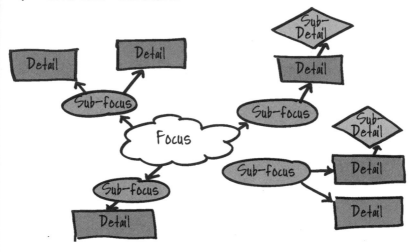

2. Story Diagramming

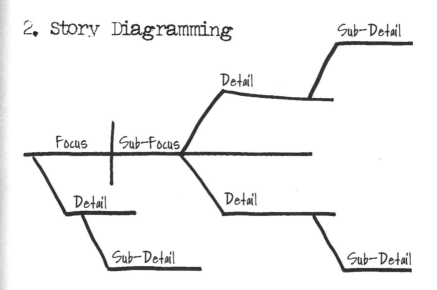

Sample Dream Interpretation

DREAM ▼

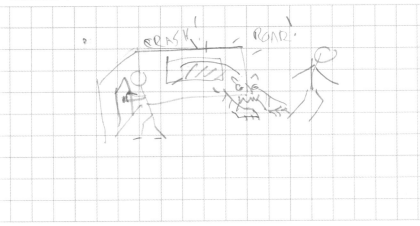

INTERPRETATION ▼

Warning dream. My business is going to suffer a set back.
It will happen after I meet 3 leaders, two of which will have
white hair. I will be okay, but what I have built will suffer. It
will seem like the business is really growing fast, until loss
of control.

MY RESPONSE ▼

Pray and ask God to stop the plans of the enemy. Ask God
what I can do to stop this. Am I trying to grow too fast?
Will the leaders influence what happens or should I have asked
their advice? Pray and ask God, who knows everything!

Personal Notes on Color

Additive Color Spectrum
Spiritual Spectrum

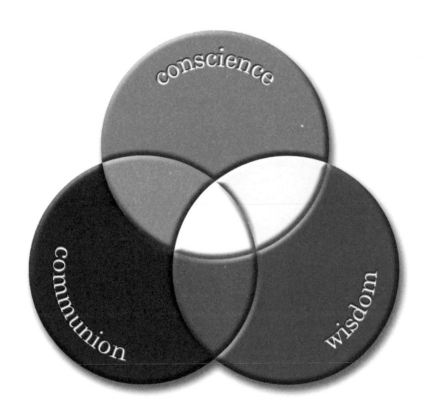

The colors are radiating.
This denotes when your spirit
fully rules over your soul.

Personal Notes on Color

Soul Spectrum

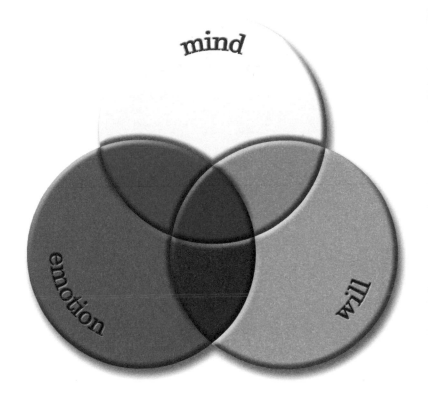

The colors are reflecting.
This denotes when your soul
rules over your spirit.

Personal Notes on Color

Additive & Subtractive Spectrum
Relationship of Soul & Spirit

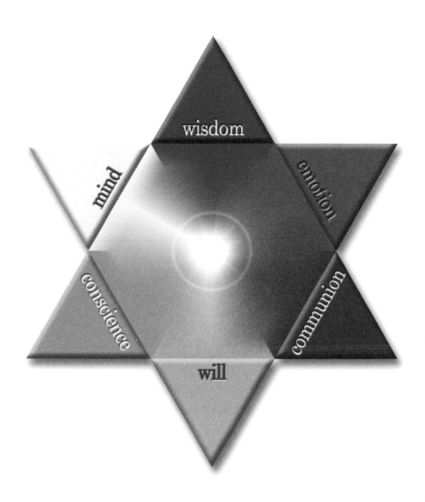

wisdom

mind

emotion

conscience

communion

will

Dream
Recording

Date_____ Title_____

Theme_____ Where was I?_____

Focus(es)_____ Sub-Focus(es)_____

_____

Color ☐ Black/White ☐ Muted ☐   _____

Recurring dream: Yes ☐   No ☐   _____

Category_____ Context: Positive ☐   Negative ☐

DREAM ▼

DREAM ▼

INTERPRETATION ▼

MY RESPONSE ▼

Date_____   Title_____

Theme_____   Where was I?_____

Focus(es)_____   Sub-Focus(es)_____

_____

Color ☐ Black/White ☐ Muted ☐   _____

Recurring dream: Yes ☐   No ☐   _____

Category_____   Context: Positive ☐ Negative ☐

DREAM ▼

DREAM ▼

INTERPRETATION ▼

MY RESPONSE ▼

Date_____ Title_____

Theme_____ Where was I?_____

Focus(es)_____ Sub-Focus(es)_____

_____

Color ☐ Black/White ☐ Muted ☐

Recurring dream: Yes ☐ No ☐

Category_____ Context: Positive ☐ Negative ☐

DREAM ▼

DREAM ▼

INTERPRETATION ▼

MY RESPONSE ▼

Date_____ Title_____

Theme_____ Where was I?_____

Focus(es)_____ Sub-Focus(es)_____

_____

Color ☐ Black/White ☐ Muted ☐   _____

Recurring dream: Yes ☐   No ☐   _____

Category_____ Context: Positive ☐ Negative ☐

DREAM ▼

DREAM ▼

INTERPRETATION ▼

MY RESPONSE ▼

Date_____ Title_____

Theme_____ Where was I?_____

Focus(es)_____ Sub-Focus(es)_____

_____

Color ☐ Black/White ☐ Muted ☐ _____

Recurring dream: Yes ☐ No ☐ _____

Category_____ Context: Positive ☐ Negative ☐

DREAM ▼

DREAM ▼

INTERPRETATION ▼

MY RESPONSE ▼

Date_____ Title_____

Theme_____ Where was I?_____

Focus(es)_____ Sub-Focus(es)_____

_____

Color ☐ Black/White ☐ Muted ☐ _____

Recurring dream: Yes ☐ No ☐ _____

Category_____ Context: Positive ☐ Negative ☐

DREAM ▼

DREAM ▼

INTERPRETATION ▼

MY RESPONSE ▼

Date_____ Title_____

Theme_____ Where was I?_____

Focus(es)_____ Sub-Focus(es)_____

_____

Color ☐ Black/White ☐ Muted ☐   _____

Recurring dream: Yes ☐   No ☐   _____

Category_____ Context: Positive ☐ Negative ☐

DREAM ▼

DREAM ▼

INTERPRETATION ▼

MY RESPONSE ▼

Date_____ Title_____

Theme_____ Where was I?_____

Focus(es)_____ Sub-Focus(es)_____

_____

Color ☐ Black/White ☐ Muted ☐   _____

Recurring dream: Yes ☐   No ☐   _____

Category_____ Context: Positive ☐ Negative ☐

DREAM ▼

DREAM ▼

INTERPRETATION ▼

MY RESPONSE ▼

Date_____ Title_____

Theme_____ Where was I?_____

Focus(es)_____ Sub-Focus(es)_____

_____

Color ☐ Black/White ☐ Muted ☐ _____

Recurring dream: Yes ☐ No ☐ _____

Category_____ Context: Positive ☐ Negative ☐

DREAM ▼

DREAM ▼

INTERPRETATION ▼

MY RESPONSE ▼

Date_____ Title_____

Theme_____ Where was I?_____

Focus(es)_____ Sub-Focus(es)_____

_____

Color ☐ Black/White ☐ Muted ☐ _____

Recurring dream: Yes ☐ No ☐ _____

Category_____ Context: Positive ☐ Negative ☐

DREAM ▼

DREAM ▼

INTERPRETATION ▼

MY RESPONSE ▼

Date_____   Title_____

Theme_____   Where was I?_____

Focus(es)_____   Sub-Focus(es)_____

_____

Color ☐ Black/White ☐ Muted ☐   _____

Recurring dream: Yes ☐   No ☐   _____

Category_____   Context: Positive ☐ Negative ☐

DREAM ▼

DREAM ▼

INTERPRETATION ▼

MY RESPONSE ▼

Date_____ Title_____

Theme_____ Where was I?_____

Focus(es)_____ Sub-Focus(es)_____

_____

Color ☐ Black/White ☐ Muted ☐ _____

Recurring dream: Yes ☐ No ☐ _____

Category_____ Context: Positive ☐ Negative ☐

DREAM ▼

DREAM ▼

INTERPRETATION ▼

MY RESPONSE ▼

Date_____   Title_____

Theme_____   Where was I?_____

Focus(es)_____   Sub-Focus(es)_____

_____   _____

Color ☐ Black/White ☐ Muted ☐   _____

Recurring dream: Yes ☐   No ☐   _____

Category_____   Context: Positive ☐ Negative ☐

DREAM ▼

DREAM ▼

INTERPRETATION ▼

MY RESPONSE ▼

Date_____   Title_____

Theme_____   Where was I?_____

Focus(es)_____   Sub-Focus(es)_____

_____   _____

Color ☐ Black/White ☐ Muted ☐   _____

Recurring dream: Yes ☐   No ☐   _____

Category_____   Context: Positive ☐ Negative ☐

DREAM ▼

DREAM ▼

INTERPRETATION ▼

MY RESPONSE ▼

Date_____ Title_____

Theme_____ Where was I?_____

Focus(es)_____ Sub-Focus(es)_____

_____

_____

Color ☐ Black/White ☐ Muted ☐ _____

Recurring dream: Yes ☐ No ☐

Category_____ Context: Positive ☐ Negative ☐

DREAM ▼

DREAM ▼

INTERPRETATION ▼

MY RESPONSE ▼

Date_____ Title_____

Theme_____ Where was I?_____

Focus(es)_____ Sub-Focus(es)_____

_____

Color ☐ Black/White ☐ Muted ☐ _____

Recurring dream: Yes ☐ No ☐ _____

Category_____ Context: Positive ☐ Negative ☐

DREAM ▼

DREAM ▼

INTERPRETATION ▼

MY RESPONSE ▼

Date_____ Title_____

Theme_____ Where was I?_____

Focus(es)_____ Sub-Focus(es)_____

_____

Color ☐ Black/White ☐ Muted ☐ _____

Recurring dream: Yes ☐ No ☐ _____

Category_____ Context: Positive ☐ Negative ☐

DREAM ▼

DREAM ▼

INTERPRETATION ▼

MY RESPONSE ▼

Date_____ Title_____

Theme_____ Where was I?_____

Focus(es)_____ Sub-Focus(es)_____

_____

Color ☐ Black/White ☐ Muted ☐ _____

Recurring dream: Yes ☐   No ☐ _____

Category_____ Context: Positive ☐ Negative ☐

DREAM ▼

DREAM ▼

INTERPRETATION ▼

MY RESPONSE ▼

Date_____ Title_____

Theme_____ Where was I?_____

Focus(es)_____ Sub-Focus(es)_____

_____

Color ☐ Black/White ☐ Muted ☐ _____

Recurring dream: Yes ☐   No ☐ _____

Category_____ Context: Positive ☐ Negative ☐

DREAM ▼

DREAM ▼

INTERPRETATION ▼

MY RESPONSE ▼

Date_____   Title_____

Theme_____   Where was I?_____

Focus(es)_____   Sub-Focus(es)_____

_____   _____

Color ☐ Black/White ☐ Muted ☐   _____

Recurring dream: Yes ☐   No ☐   _____

Category_____   Context: Positive ☐ Negative ☐

DREAM ▼

DREAM ▼

INTERPRETATION ▼

MY RESPONSE ▼

Date_____ Title_____

Theme_____ Where was I?_____

Focus(es)_____ Sub-Focus(es)_____

_____ _____

Color ☐ Black/White ☐ Muted ☐ _____

Recurring dream: Yes ☐ No ☐ _____

Category_____ Context: Positive ☐ Negative ☐

DREAM ▼

DREAM ▼

INTERPRETATION ▼

MY RESPONSE ▼

Date_____ Title_____

Theme_____ Where was I?_____

Focus(es)_____ Sub-Focus(es)_____

_____

Color ☐ Black/White ☐ Muted ☐

_____

Recurring dream: Yes ☐ No ☐

_____

Category_____ Context: Positive ☐ Negative ☐

DREAM ▼

DREAM ▼

INTERPRETATION ▼

MY RESPONSE ▼

Date_____ Title_____

Theme_____ Where was I?_____

Focus(es)_____ Sub-Focus(es)_____

_____ _____

Color ☐ Black/White ☐ Muted ☐ _____

Recurring dream: Yes ☐ No ☐ _____

Category_____ Context: Positive ☐ Negative ☐

DREAM ▼

DREAM ▼

INTERPRETATION ▼

MY RESPONSE ▼

Date_____ Title_____

Theme_____ Where was I?_____

Focus(es)_____ Sub-Focus(es)_____

_____

Color ☐ Black/White ☐ Muted ☐

Recurring dream: Yes ☐ No ☐ _____

Category_____ Context: Positive ☐ Negative ☐

DREAM ▼

DREAM ▼

INTERPRETATION ▼

MY RESPONSE ▼

Date_____ Title_____

Theme_____ Where was I?_____

Focus(es)_____ Sub-Focus(es)_____

_____ _____

Color ☐ Black/White ☐ Muted ☐   _____

Recurring dream: Yes ☐   No ☐   _____

Category_____ Context: Positive ☐ Negative ☐

DREAM ▼

DREAM ▼

INTERPRETATION ▼

MY RESPONSE ▼

Date_____ Title_____

Theme_____ Where was I?_____

Focus(es)_____ Sub-Focus(es)_____

_____

Color ☐ Black/White ☐ Muted ☐ _____

Recurring dream: Yes ☐ No ☐ _____

Category_____ Context: Positive ☐ Negative ☐

DREAM ▼

DREAM ▼

INTERPRETATION ▼

MY RESPONSE ▼

Date_____ Title_____

Theme_____ Where was I?_____

Focus(es)_____ Sub-Focus(es)_____

_____ _____

Color ☐ Black/White ☐ Muted ☐ _____

Recurring dream: Yes ☐ No ☐ _____

Category_____ Context: Positive ☐ Negative ☐

DREAM ▼

DREAM ▼

INTERPRETATION ▼

MY RESPONSE ▼

Date_____ Title_____

Theme_____ Where was I?_____

Focus(es)_____ Sub-Focus(es)_____

_____

Color ☐ Black/White ☐ Muted ☐ _____

Recurring dream: Yes ☐ No ☐ _____

Category_____ Context: Positive ☐ Negative ☐

DREAM ▼

DREAM ▼

INTERPRETATION ▼

MY RESPONSE ▼

Date_____ Title_____

Theme_____ Where was I?_____

Focus(es)_____ Sub-Focus(es)_____

_____

Color ☐ Black/White ☐ Muted ☐ _____

Recurring dream: Yes ☐   No ☐ _____

Category_____ Context: Positive ☐ Negative ☐

DREAM ▼

DREAM ▼

INTERPRETATION ▼

MY RESPONSE ▼

Date_____ Title_____

Theme_____ Where was I?_____

Focus(es)_____ Sub-Focus(es)_____

_____

Color ☐ Black/White ☐ Muted ☐   _____

Recurring dream: Yes ☐   No ☐   _____

Category_____ Context: Positive ☐ Negative ☐

DREAM ▼

DREAM ▼

INTERPRETATION ▼

MY RESPONSE ▼

Date_____ Title_____

Theme_____ Where was I?_____

Focus(es)_____ Sub-Focus(es)_____

_____ _____

Color ☐ Black/White ☐ Muted ☐ _____

Recurring dream: Yes ☐   No ☐ _____

Category_____ Context: Positive ☐ Negative ☐

DREAM ▼

DREAM ▼

INTERPRETATION ▼

MY RESPONSE ▼

Date_____   Title_____

Theme_____   Where was I?_____

Focus(es)_____   Sub-Focus(es)_____

_____

Color ☐ Black/White ☐ Muted ☐   _____

Recurring dream: Yes ☐   No ☐   _____

Category_____   Context: Positive ☐ Negative ☐

DREAM ▼

DREAM ▼

INTERPRETATION ▼

MY RESPONSE ▼

Date_____ Title_____

Theme_____ Where was I?_____

Focus(es)_____ Sub-Focus(es)_____

_____

Color ☐ Black/White ☐ Muted ☐ _____

Recurring dream: Yes ☐ No ☐ _____

Category_____ Context: Positive ☐ Negative ☐

DREAM ▼

DREAM ▼

INTERPRETATION ▼

MY RESPONSE ▼

Date_____ Title_____

Theme_____ Where was I?_____

Focus(es)_____ Sub-Focus(es)_____

_____

Color ☐ Black/White ☐ Muted ☐   _____

Recurring dream: Yes ☐   No ☐   _____

Category_____ Context: Positive ☐ Negative ☐

DREAM ▼

DREAM ▼

INTERPRETATION ▼

MY RESPONSE ▼

Date_____ Title_____

Theme_____ Where was I?_____

Focus(es)_____ Sub-Focus(es)_____

_____ _____

Color ☐ Black/White ☐ Muted ☐ _____

Recurring dream: Yes ☐   No ☐ _____

Category_____ Context: Positive ☐   Negative ☐

DREAM ▼

DREAM ▼

INTERPRETATION ▼

MY RESPONSE ▼

Date_____ Title_____

Theme_____ Where was I?_____

Focus(es)_____ Sub-Focus(es)_____

_____

Color ☐ Black/White ☐ Muted ☐ _____

Recurring dream: Yes ☐ No ☐ _____

Category_____ Context: Positive ☐ Negative ☐

DREAM ▼

DREAM ▼

INTERPRETATION ▼

MY RESPONSE ▼

Date_____ Title_____

Theme_____ Where was I?_____

Focus(es)_____ Sub-Focus(es)_____

_____

Color ☐ Black/White ☐ Muted ☐ _____

Recurring dream: Yes ☐ No ☐ _____

Category_____ Context: Positive ☐ Negative ☐

DREAM ▼

DREAM ▼

INTERPRETATION ▼

MY RESPONSE ▼

Date_____   Title_____

Theme_____   Where was I?_____

Focus(es)_____   Sub-Focus(es)_____

_____

Color ☐ Black/White ☐ Muted ☐   _____

Recurring dream: Yes ☐   No ☐   _____

Category_____   Context: Positive ☐   Negative ☐

DREAM ▼

DREAM ▼

INTERPRETATION ▼

MY RESPONSE ▼

Date_____ Title_____

Theme_____ Where was I?_____

Focus(es)_____ Sub-Focus(es)_____

_____

Color ☐ Black/White ☐ Muted ☐ _____

Recurring dream: Yes ☐   No ☐ _____

Category_____ Context: Positive ☐ Negative ☐

DREAM ▼

DREAM ▼

INTERPRETATION ▼

MY RESPONSE ▼

Date_____ Title_____

Theme_____ Where was I?_____

Focus(es)_____ Sub-Focus(es)_____

_____

Color ☐ Black/White ☐ Muted ☐ _____

Recurring dream: Yes ☐   No ☐ _____

Category_____ Context: Positive ☐ Negative ☐

DREAM ▼

DREAM ▼

INTERPRETATION ▼

MY RESPONSE ▼

Date_____ Title_____

Theme_____ Where was I?_____

Focus(es)_____ Sub-Focus(es)_____

_____

Color ☐ Black/White ☐ Muted ☐ _____

Recurring dream: Yes ☐ No ☐ _____

Category_____ Context: Positive ☐ Negative ☐

DREAM ▼

DREAM ▼

INTERPRETATION ▼

MY RESPONSE ▼

Date_____ Title_____

Theme_____ Where was I?_____

Focus(es)_____ Sub-Focus(es)_____

_____ _____

Color ☐ Black/White ☐ Muted ☐ _____

Recurring dream: Yes ☐   No ☐ _____

Category_____ Context: Positive ☐ Negative ☐

DREAM ▼

DREAM ▼

INTERPRETATION ▼

MY RESPONSE ▼

Date_____ Title_____

Theme_____ Where was I?_____

Focus(es)_____ Sub-Focus(es)_____

_____ _____

Color ☐ Black/White ☐ Muted ☐ _____

Recurring dream: Yes ☐   No ☐ _____

Category_____ Context: Positive ☐ Negative ☐

DREAM ▼

DREAM ▼

INTERPRETATION ▼

MY RESPONSE ▼

Date_____ Title_____

Theme_____ Where was I?_____

Focus(es)_____ Sub-Focus(es)_____

_____

Color ☐ Black/White ☐ Muted ☐

_____

Recurring dream: Yes ☐   No ☐

_____

Category_____ Context: Positive ☐ Negative ☐

DREAM ▼

DREAM ▼

INTERPRETATION ▼

MY RESPONSE ▼

Date_____   Title_____

Theme_____   Where was I?_____

Focus(es)_____   Sub-Focus(es)_____

_____

Color ☐ Black/White ☐ Muted ☐   _____

Recurring dream: Yes ☐   No ☐   _____

Category_____   Context: Positive ☐ Negative ☐

DREAM ▼

DREAM ▼

INTERPRETATION ▼

MY RESPONSE ▼

Date_____ Title_____

Theme_____ Where was I?_____

Focus(es)_____ Sub-Focus(es)_____

_____

Color ☐ Black/White ☐ Muted ☐ _____

Recurring dream: Yes ☐   No ☐ _____

Category_____ Context: Positive ☐ Negative ☐

DREAM ▼

DREAM ▼

INTERPRETATION ▼

MY RESPONSE ▼

Date_____ Title_____

Theme_____ Where was I?_____

Focus(es)_____ Sub-Focus(es)_____

_____ _____

Color ☐ Black/White ☐ Muted ☐ _____

Recurring dream: Yes ☐ No ☐ _____

Category_____ Context: Positive ☐ Negative ☐

DREAM ▼

DREAM ▼

INTERPRETATION ▼

MY RESPONSE ▼

Date_____ Title_____

Theme_____ Where was I?_____

Focus(es)_____ Sub-Focus(es)_____

_____

Color ☐ Black/White ☐ Muted ☐ _____

Recurring dream: Yes ☐ No ☐ _____

Category_____ Context: Positive ☐ Negative ☐

DREAM ▼

DREAM ▼

INTERPRETATION ▼

MY RESPONSE ▼

Date_____ Title_____

Theme_____ Where was I?_____

Focus(es)_____ Sub-Focus(es)_____

_____

Color ☐ Black/White ☐ Muted ☐   _____

Recurring dream: Yes ☐   No ☐   _____

Category_____ Context: Positive ☐   Negative ☐

DREAM ▼

DREAM ▼

INTERPRETATION ▼

MY RESPONSE ▼

Date_____ Title_____

Theme_____ Where was I?_____

Focus(es)_____ Sub-Focus(es)_____

_____

Color ☐ Black/White ☐ Muted ☐ _____

Recurring dream: Yes ☐ No ☐ _____

Category_____ Context: Positive ☐ Negative ☐

DREAM ▼

DREAM ▼

INTERPRETATION ▼

MY RESPONSE ▼

Date_____   Title_____

Theme_____   Where was I?_____

Focus(es)_____   Sub-Focus(es)_____

_____   _____

Color ☐ Black/White ☐ Muted ☐   _____

Recurring dream: Yes ☐   No ☐   _____

Category_____   Context: Positive ☐   Negative ☐

DREAM ▼

DREAM ▼

INTERPRETATION ▼

MY RESPONSE ▼

Date_____   Title_____

Theme_____   Where was I?_____

Focus(es)_____   Sub-Focus(es)_____

_____

Color ☐ Black/White ☐ Muted ☐   _____

Recurring dream: Yes ☐   No ☐   _____

Category_____   Context: Positive ☐ Negative ☐

DREAM ▼

DREAM ▼

INTERPRETATION ▼

MY RESPONSE ▼

Date_____ Title_____

Theme_____ Where was I?_____

Focus(es)_____ Sub-Focus(es)_____

_____

Color ☐ Black/White ☐ Muted ☐ _____

Recurring dream: Yes ☐ No ☐ _____

Category_____ Context: Positive ☐ Negative ☐

DREAM ▼

DREAM ▼

INTERPRETATION ▼

MY RESPONSE ▼

Date_____ Title_____

Theme_____ Where was I?_____

Focus(es)_____ Sub-Focus(es)_____

_____

Color ☐ Black/White ☐ Muted ☐ _____

Recurring dream: Yes ☐ No ☐ _____

Category_____ Context: Positive ☐ Negative ☐

DREAM ▼

DREAM ▼

INTERPRETATION ▼

MY RESPONSE ▼

Date_____ Title_____

Theme_____ Where was I?_____

Focus(es)_____ Sub-Focus(es)_____

_____

Color ☐ Black/White ☐ Muted ☐ _____

Recurring dream: Yes ☐ No ☐ _____

Category_____ Context: Positive ☐ Negative ☐

DREAM ▼

DREAM ▼

INTERPRETATION ▼

MY RESPONSE ▼

Date_____   Title_____

Theme_____   Where was I?_____

Focus(es)_____   Sub-Focus(es)_____

_____

Color ☐ Black/White ☐ Muted ☐   _____

Recurring dream: Yes ☐   No ☐   _____

Category_____   Context: Positive ☐ Negative ☐

DREAM ▼

DREAM ▼

INTERPRETATION ▼

MY RESPONSE ▼

Date_____ Title_____

Theme_____ Where was I?_____

Focus(es)_____ Sub-Focus(es)_____

_____

Color ☐ Black/White ☐ Muted ☐ _____

Recurring dream: Yes ☐   No ☐ _____

Category_____ Context: Positive ☐ Negative ☐

DREAM ▼

DREAM ▼

INTERPRETATION ▼

MY RESPONSE ▼

Date_____   Title_____

Theme_____   Where was I?_____

Focus(es)_____   Sub-Focus(es)_____

_____

Color ☐ Black/White ☐ Muted ☐   _____

Recurring dream: Yes ☐   No ☐   _____

Category_____   Context: Positive ☐ Negative ☐

DREAM ▼

DREAM ▼

INTERPRETATION ▼

MY RESPONSE ▼

Date_____ Title_____

Theme_____ Where was I?_____

Focus(es)_____ Sub-Focus(es)_____

_____

Color ☐ Black/White ☐ Muted ☐ _____

Recurring dream: Yes ☐ No ☐ _____

Category_____ Context: Positive ☐ Negative ☐

DREAM ▼

DREAM ▼

INTERPRETATION ▼

MY RESPONSE ▼

Date_____ Title_____

Theme_____ Where was I?_____

Focus(es)_____ Sub-Focus(es)_____

_____ _____

Color ☐ Black/White ☐ Muted ☐   _____

Recurring dream: Yes ☐   No ☐   _____

Category_____ Context: Positive ☐ Negative ☐

DREAM ▼

DREAM ▼

INTERPRETATION ▼

MY RESPONSE ▼

Date_____ Title_____

Theme_____ Where was I?_____

Focus(es)_____ Sub-Focus(es)_____

_____

Color ☐ Black/White ☐ Muted ☐

_____

Recurring dream: Yes ☐   No ☐

_____

Category_____ Context: Positive ☐ Negative ☐

DREAM ▼

DREAM ▼

INTERPRETATION ▼

MY RESPONSE ▼

Date_____   Title_____

Theme_____   Where was I?_____

Focus(es)_____   Sub-Focus(es)_____

_____   _____

Color ☐ Black/White ☐ Muted ☐   _____

Recurring dream: Yes ☐   No ☐   _____

Category_____   Context: Positive ☐ Negative ☐

DREAM ▼

DREAM ▼

INTERPRETATION ▼

MY RESPONSE ▼

Date_____   Title_____

Theme_____   Where was I?_____

Focus(es)_____   Sub-Focus(es)_____

_____   _____

Color ☐   Black/White ☐   Muted ☐   _____

Recurring dream: Yes ☐   No ☐   _____

Category_____   Context: Positive ☐   Negative ☐

DREAM ▼

DREAM ▼

INTERPRETATION ▼

MY RESPONSE ▼

Date_____   Title_____

Theme_____   Where was I?_____

Focus(es)_____   Sub-Focus(es)_____

_____   _____

Color ☐   Black/White ☐   Muted ☐   _____

Recurring dream: Yes ☐   No ☐   _____

Category_____   Context: Positive ☐   Negative ☐

DREAM ▼

DREAM ▼

INTERPRETATION ▼

MY RESPONSE ▼

Date_____ Title_____

Theme_____ Where was I?_____

Focus(es)_____ Sub-Focus(es)_____

_____ _____

Color ☐ Black/White ☐ Muted ☐ _____

Recurring dream: Yes ☐ No ☐ _____

Category_____ Context: Positive ☐ Negative ☐

DREAM ▼

DREAM ▼

INTERPRETATION ▼

MY RESPONSE ▼

Dream Vocabulary

DREAM VOCABULARY

Date	Metaphor/Elements	Color	Feeling	Activity	Meaning

DREAM VOCABULARY

Date	Metaphor/Elements	Color	Feeling	Activity	Meaning

DREAM VOCABULARY

Date	Metaphor/Elements	Color	Feeling	Activity	Meaning

DREAM VOCABULARY _____

Date	Metaphor/Elements	Color	Feeling	Activity	Meaning

DREAM VOCABULARY

Date	Metaphor/Elements	Color	Feeling	Activity	Meaning

DREAM VOCABULARY

Date	Metaphor/Elements	Color	Feeling	Activity	Meaning

DREAM VOCABULARY

Date	Metaphor/Elements	Color	Feeling	Activity	Meaning

DREAM VOCABULARY

Date	Metaphor/Elements	Color	Feeling	Activity	Meaning

DREAM VOCABULARY

Date	Metaphor/Elements	Color	Feeling	Activity	Meaning

About the Author

JOHN PAUL JACKSON HAS been at the forefront of prophetic ministry for more than 20 years. As founder of The Streams Institute for Spiritual Development, John Paul travels around the world teaching on The Art of Hearing God, dreams, visions, and the supernatural. He has authored several books, and appeared on *The 700 Club*, *This Is Your Day* with Benny Hinn, Cornerstone Television, God Digital, and Daystar Television.

John Paul has served as senior pastor of two churches. He has also served on the pastoral staff at the Vineyard Christian Fellowship in Anaheim, California and at Metro Christian Fellowship in Kansas City, Missouri.

It was his great love for the Body of Christ that prompted John Paul to launch Streams Ministries International, an outreach that endeavors to encourage, motivate, and equip individuals to walk in greater maturity, wisdom, character, and holiness. Streams Ministries seeks to touch people around the world, declaring the marvelous message of God's love. As people have experienced the supernatural power of God, lives continue to be transformed.

Books by
John Paul Jackson

Unmasking the Jezebel Spirit

Buying & Selling the Souls of Our Children

Needless Casualties of War

Audiotapes by
John Paul Jackson

Understanding Dreams and Visions

Spiritual Dilemmas

Prophetic Reformation

Passage to Intimacy

How to Be a Prophet Without Being a Jerk!

Expecting the Miraculous

Wisdom and the Prophetic Journey

Preparing for Your Visitation

Message to America

Naturally Supernatural

Understanding Dreams & Visions

Explore the world of dreams. Unravel the
mysteries of dream interpretation in this inspiring
series and discover how to apply God-given insights
in your waking life. You won't want to miss these
fascinating insights from a gifted dream expert.

(Six audiotapes in an album.)
Retail $36.00

Streams Institute
for Spiritual Development^{SM}

At Streams, our desire is to **awaken** a
deeper understanding of knowing God.
We offer a **dynamic** learning environment with
courses ranging from beginner to advanced.
Join us as we embark on an **exciting** journey
into deeper revelations of GOD!

COURSE 101:
The Art of Hearing God

Designed as an introductory course, you will be taught skills to hear God's voice and develop greater intimacy with Him. This course consists of 21 hours. (Also available as a home study course)

COURSE 201:
Dreams and Visions

A powerful source of insight and inspiration, this advanced course digs deeper into the wonder and awe of the supernatural. It provides a fascinating glimpse of how God speaks to you through dreams and visions. This course consists of 21 hours.
(Prerequisite: Course 101)

COURSE 202:
Advanced Workshop in Dream Interpretation

Full of supernatural insight and excitement, this advanced course delves deeper into dream interpretation and developing your own dream vocabulary. You also practice interpreting the dreams of others. This course consists of 21 hours.
(Prerequisite: Course 201)

To **register**, call toll free
(U.S. and Canada) 1-888-441-8080.
Or send an email to isd@streamsministries.com.
You can also visit us on the web at
www.streamsministries.com.

We hope you enjoyed this
publication from Streams.
If you would like to receive a
free catalog featuring other
Streams products, please contact:

Streams Ministries International
P.O.Box 550
North Sutton, NH 03260
1-888-441-8080
www.streamsministries.com